MY ACTIVE IMAGINATION

A book about fitness, rhyme and family time!

Spot Snickerdoodle the Caterpillar!

Cover and Illustrations by Paige Wannop

First Printing, 2017

Cataloguing in Publication Data Rubeniuk, Karlyn, 2017 - My Active Imagination

ISBN 978-0-9959634-1-2

Bob & Sandra Speight, Sonya Rubeniuk for Kaeli, Addison, Cadence & Stephen, Brock Speight for Brooklyn & Braya, Sharla Curle for Logan & Keyana, Jodi Hrymak for Emma & Bria, Shari Haverstock for Keirstyn & Sydney, Val Swain, Susan Palmer, Granny Sue for Kiera, Caeli, Liam & Brinn, Granny Sue for Marie-Claude, Alex, Ben & Sam, Lisa Klippenstein, Paula Stirling, Aimee Holland for Adie & Carsen, Michelle Osudar for Bryce & Ashton, Brenda Roth, Maureen Miller, Darlene Twerdochlib, Judy Wesley, Anne Boychuk, Jennifer Elliott, Charlene Bazarian, Jillian Michaels, Heidi, Lukensia & Phoenix, Kenta Seki, Jaime McFaden for Sophia, Anita Julia Bognar for Timothy, Caitlin, Elijah & Briana, Abnita, Basheerah Ahmad, Nichole Pellant, Debbie Myers, Joyce for Cathy & Mike, Kasia Murthy for Jakub, Samuel & Samantha, Sophie Louise May, Samantha Mawbey for Ava, Jamie Graham, Marylou Desbiens, Dianne Berentsen for Cathi, Kimberly, Christina & Karri, Julie Sothern, Lesley Sarver, Becca Yorinks, Patti Tokar, Nomkhosi Mathebula, Dawn Allen, Dana Barton, Kerstin Diederich, Heather Adkins for Alyssa & Jacob, Elle Meyer, Erin Heywood for Samantha & Daniel, Amanda Dixon for Londyn & Lylah, Kishmer Laurencin, Donna Crispin for Isla & Noah, Anne Ibnusantosa for Tamara, Elena Chereches, Emma Compton for Mikey & Danny, Laura Felde for Nick & Jorge, Lisa Humphreys, Natalie Phillips for Caleb, Morgan & Leo, Geetika Tandon for Shrey, Louise Hatswell for Joel & Jordan, Deb Bouland for Lindy, Nancy Francis, Tracy Steadwood for Ellen, Heather Harrington for Natalie, Victoria Gonzales for Bela & Mila, Silvia Jasso for Yaretzi, Kay Ahumada for Emily & Mila, Daniela Burow for Jacqueline & Sebastian, Kaella MacMillan for Callum & Eve, Nancy K & Adam A, Purvi Thaker Choksey for Riyann & Arya, Jessica Hill for Haley & Mason, Danielle Rochette for Tyler & Taryn, Tonya Lyle for my buddy Landon Howard, Michelle Neitzel for Alexis & Adam, Kelly Duke for Riley & Natalie, Anita Narine for Renaldo, Romero & Romillio, Sara Hart for Brian & Benjamin, Victoria Long, Shelsetta Douglas, Kristina Pogorelc for Ava & Jacie, Nichole Ho for Emersyn, Hudson & Everett, Suzanne Everly for Taylor & Kyle, Courtney Jones for Alexis, Kristi Sutton for Nyla, Debbie Kalstek for Luke & Jenna, Tamara Thompson for Kaisha, Linda Munoz for Jason & Nicholas, Kerry & Isabelle Mcquade, Andria Taylor for Arianna, Eileen Dixon for Jack, Jeannie Petropoulos & Georgia, Hazel Bridle for James, Emily, Bella & Oli, Nevine Mohamed for Abdullah, Lazuli Mykulak, Trish Willems, Rabia Ahmed for Zoey, Cindy Cleaver for Jordan & Aubrey, Kim for Henry & Harvey, Kate Miller for Nico, Charlotte Coit for David & Christian, Civita Brensinger, Lauren Stewart, Punam & Hitayu, Robin Edwards, Lynne Gottier, Lori Jones, Dimple Kakade, Noel for Raven, Pierce, Kira, Saige & Grayson, Heather Boyce for Brittany & Nicolas, Lorna Garney, Sarah & Marleigh Mitchell, Bec O'Neill, Melissa Goldstein, Amy Clark for Harleigh & Kira, Rosalinda Pacheco for Amy & Alex, Sharmon Savoie, Katie Badgley, Ruth, Anthony & Alexa McDonald, Susan Wright for Ashleigh, Karen Freeman, Cat Coyle for Cherokee, Tiffany Ross for Reegan, Sara Duenas for Olivia, JJ & Mateo, Sumedha Vinayak, Tara Gleason, Rosa Garcia for Violette Rose, Muriel Merritt for Maddilyn, Kenton & Kylie, Olga Cuaresma for Blaise, Alissa Purcell for Calder, Sarah Williams for Joey, Sara Bessey, Susanna Thong for Jeremy & Julian, Cherise Erdmann for Aaliyah, Emily, Levi & Benjamim, Michaela Blomqvist for Knut & Emilia, Thabi Letsunyane, Ruth Harkness, Karen Crosby Priddy, Namthip for Theva, Julie Roberson for Cori, Owen & Makenna, Sharlon McSheen for Shannon, Oisín & Tobias, Brandy Bianco, Maggie Mulholland, Catharina Breu, Kellie Sneddon-Wood, Michelle Thompson for Aidan & Alaina, Patti Harms for Isabella & Kaitlyn, Cristy & Vivian Tejon, Anu Mäkinen, Candida Dias, Christy Soto, Vanessa Polk for Abigail, Lynn Stein for all who can't workout, Danielle Grafsky for Ivan & Lana, Andrea Timmins for Olivia, Freida & Abby, Mary Jude Schmitz for Katie, Renee & Billy, Kristen Davis for Delaney & Gavin, Donna Biderman, Helen Murray for Kara & Connor, Esley, Ashlyn, Isla & Owen, Jamie Pflug. Dawn Chetto for Zachary & Marcus, Helene Foster Platke for Meghan, Danielle, Miranda & Samantha

For my son Kyler, who always hated to read but loved to snuggle while I read to him.
"Let the stress of the day wash away."

Thank you to my husband Kevin, the love of my life who shows his love for his family
in every possible way and loves me even when I have had coffee.

Thank you to my parents, who to this day are always there for me and believe in all my crazy shenanigans.

And to Lixsi and Jodi for being my biggest cheerleaders on this journey.

*Have fun finding imaginative
ways to stay FIT!*

Karlyn Rubeniuk

Did you stop to wonder who he was in a rush to meet?

Or maybe just a friend of his, who has a frog that sings?

Nah! He's working out today to keep himself in shape,

for when his kids ask to go waterskiing on the lake!

Did you think she was in a race with someone she just had to beat?

Or was she being chased by a giant pumpkin pie,

a purple alligator or a goldfish in the sky?

So when her kids are playing tag, she can play along!

Have you ever seen a swimmer, splashing across a lake?

Ever stop to wonder why it wasn't a boat she chose to take?

Or did it sink to the bottom because it was broken and old?

And if you haven't lately, don't you think you should?

Change is possible.
Start by imagining yourself as who you wish to be.

If the caterpillar didn't dream of becoming a butterfly,
it would never have bothered to spin its cocoon.

Sara Helmus for Chloe & Ben, Madeeha Syed for Zainab, Maria Garcia, Christina Spoula, Hannah Gantt, Tamie Cox, Robin Ranaphyali, Sharon Tarantino, Nancy Broncaccio, Anita Tardugno, Amy Gerrits, Erin McGregor, Lety Zielinski, Gabriela Abudo, Amanda Grant, Wendy Clarke, Susan Buttermore, Meranda Shepard for Carter, Grace & Paisley, Simona Oblak, Christine Watters, Meridith Pajak-Gonzales, Amanda DuLong, Grace Maria Elston, Brandi Bain, Frances Gann, Linda Lopez, Whitney Landsteiner, Mary Beach for Trinity, Ausha Marie, Michelle Den Boer, Kay Ahumada, Laurie Scaglione, Yvonne Merlotti, Numila Alvarez, Brenda Kniseley, Brenda Barrett, Aicha Kermoury Bish, Jennifer Austin, Jessi Milam, Carrie Ahern, Anita Harvie, Ashley Singh, Carol Perry, Carly Taylor, Chelsey Vickary, Amanda Amburgey, Leslie Glandon, Rosa Cordua, Dawn Reema Al-Hasan, Melodie Clements, Jennie Chambers, Jennifer Robin Jones, Meg Spoon, Lori Schmalzried Mikulka, Halcyon Learned, Rose Nunn, Becky Binsfeld, Katie B, Karla Mausejack, Jennifer Farnham, Kate Blackstone, Courtney Puckett, Penny Schumers, Kathryn Reid, Santina Howlett, Jasmin Wunder, Kimberly Ann, Suzanne Drummond, Eileen Dixon, Mary Begovich, Kimberly Kozak, Aida Bajramovic, Sandi Coulter, Laura Cameron, Jennifer Dourado, Sam Stevens, Sharon Klooster, Kari Brown, Michelle Peterson, Chrstina Selzer, Adrian Vaillancourt-Gum, Trish Willems, Mellisa Weigand, Dagmar Van Twillert, Jen DePaull, Ameta Parlin, Anabel Fuentes, Anna Hulme, Alica Daniels, Cindy Straka, Agata Betlej, Jacqueline Llovet, Kathryn Colter. Laura Harrison, Alicia Harris, Libby Oye, Kaylee Jobin, Natalie Phillips ,Angie Bergunson, Lindsay Unrau, Caitlin Cormack, Tricia Jenkins, Kelley Cloutman, Lindsay Reid, Jenn Heibein, Heather Blasius, Roberta Murroni, Cheryl Gamble, Justina Schultz, Nicolle Marie, Heather Santistevan, Valentina Mladenova, Sara Pruitt, Kirsty Phillips, Sam Reynolds, Andrea Timmins, Lauren Collier, Samantha Bechmann, Alicia Thrasher, Angela Cash, Chantal Pelletier, Cathy Meader, Maria Collins, Britnie Simmons, Holly McKee, Emilie Maisonobe,Carol Rogalski, Kate Miller, Dina Girard, Courtney Zuidema, Jennifer Sanow, Kerry Melson, Mary Plein , Valerie Melbrod, Jaymeejo Rhodes, Lynda Satre, Jennifer Ward Ryan, Amy Wigs, Courtney Jones, Jodi Newcom, Carol Weaver, Vanessa Nidhan-Maharaj, Greta Silva, Stacey Georganas-Mihalopoulos, Alexandra Marchuk, Janice Folk, Sally Hasted, Kristina Soliz, Lisa Arndt, Jen Nichols, Georgia Hale, Michelle Davidson, Tamra Alvord, Nikki Klautt, Laurin Simpson, Jenn Barr, Kelly Shellabarger Flees, Soha AbuOudeh, Karen McMahon, Svatia Mueller, Alyssa Lawson, Teshua Bowen, Carlee Welch, Cyndi Reitenbaugh, Julie Camacho, Kimberly Bishop, Tonya Lange, Pamela Dunning, Mela Williams, Kate Buwalda-Dorsey, Daisy Seymour, Lucia Guardia, Meissa Foust, Andrea Thompson, Ellen Kiely Allen, Joanie Templeton, Kelly Wolner, Judy Cardenas, Melanie Schuckman, Alma Cation, Sara Schurman, Jenn Oliver, Tracy Lambert, Nina Berner, Joanne Lyons , Tanya Farrell, Amy Johnson, Grace Zamora, Mara Iacobo, Davina Jenkins, Mari Love, Beth Megan, Allison Cracchiolo, Anna Rushton Olatunbosun for her little miracle, Amber Edwards, Carolynn McCarty, Shannon Kepner, Pamela Samsukal, Angelina Clarke, Sarah Jayne, Myra Musgrove, Roberta Murroni, Lisa Coles, Corinne Vance, Heather Harrington, Rene Holdridge, Audrey Aken, , Brandi Bain, Lety Zielinski, Kayla Haerter-Wells, Wendy Clarke, Kaylee Jobin, Heather Fequet, Brenda Barrett, Jaclyn Dorney, Robbie Shea, Joanne Lyons, Kelly Kuester, Camillee Moreira, Ashley Roberson, Brooklyn Morrill, Dawn Reema Al-Hasan, Marie –Soleil Martel, Victoria Fortier, Vsh Kaur for Avshaannya & Jaydaiv, Martillini, Jill Drascic, Catherine Raymond, Nicola Fisher, Rene Holdridge, Nikki Mills, Miriam Cramer, Melodie Clements, Jennifer Jones, Jennifer Dourado, Cyndi Straka, Cyndi Tuschinski for Samantha, Stanley, Sophia, Shawn, Susan, Madeline, William, Charlie, Isabelle, Jack, Eisaac, Tanner, Rhyann, Trevor, Trish, Doug & Erin Wannop, Brent Lowrie, Perri Gardner, Fallon Beaver, Rebecca Kash for Ashley, Isabelle Zammit, Arlene Aaøyen, Lynne Irwin, Dumakude Smangele Smash, Rachel Martinez for Ben, Robin Hur, Kola & to all the other amazing JMWJunkies who inspire me every day! Thank you! May all our families be active and healthy!

Made in the USA
Lexington, KY
31 October 2017